i need HELP, TOO!

by
VIC LEE

**Andrews McMeel
Publishing**

Kansas City

The bigamy trial of Prince Charming.

At the Theoretical Diner.

"Sounds to me like you're addicted to counseling. So why don't we try three sessions a week for the first couple years and see how recovery goes."

The night watchman.

Sheep farm inventory.

"It was a little drab in here until someone suggested I hang a few paintings."

THE PRESIDENT HAS ORDERED THE REDUCTION OF OUR NUCLEAR MISSLES THROUGHOUT THE WORLD.

one day at the Pentagon

V. LEE

I KNOW. WE'VE GOT TO COME UP WITH A PLAN.

FOR PROMOTING WORLD PEACE?

NO. FOR GETTING THE ENEMY TO STAND CLOSER TOGETHER.

Why executioners don't make good photographers.

Buying used paint.

"You better start talking fast, buster! Now how did blonde fur get in that hairball?"

The truth about Memorex.

Buzz Aldrin: second man on the moon.

**Toby Silus misses the concept
of food stamps.**

"Gee, Medusa, your hair looks so
nice and full-bodied."

Reebok goes into the underwear business.

"It's a device for taking the temperature of infants. What do you suggest I do with it?"

"If you look out the left side of the plane, you'll see tonight's movie, which looks like *Return of the Sorority Party Mutants*."

"True, the results of the taste comparison are quite obvious, but it would be nice to get some kind of live endorsement."

How to tell when there's too much
nudity in the movies.

"Dang! My arm fell asleep at work,
and now it's going to be up all night."

"It's part of that '70s revival kick."

Dr. Kevorkian's garden.

"Hey, ask anyone here. You said eight tiny reindeer."

Life Lesson #77 – for accountants: Never list occupation as "bookkeeper."

The Neighborhood Watch Program.

The trouble with Italian food.

28

Pamela Anderson writes another _Baywatch_ script.

"I probably should have warned you. The climate control is _real_ sensitive."

Though lacking in speed and skill, Quasimodo was the only member of the Notre Dame wrestling team to never get pinned.

Houdini's greatest challenge.

ALWAYS PLAN BACKWARDS WITH WOMEN. IF THE MOVIE'S AT 10, I PICK HER UP AT 9. THAT MEANS I SHOWER AT 8, WHICH MEANS I'M WORKING OUT AT 7, WHICH THEN MEANS I LEAVE WORK AT 6 . . .

THAT MEANS I GET TO WORK AT 9, WHICH, OF COURSE, MEANS I'M ASLEEP THE NIGHT BEFORE BY MIDNIGHT, MEANING . . .

. . . NOW I'M LATE. I CAN'T MAKE IT.

LET ME GET THIS STRAIGHT. I'M SUPPOSED TO TAKE ONE OF THESE PILLS EVERY DAY FOR THE REST OF MY LIFE?

DON'T FRET IT. LOTS OF PEOPLE HAVE TO TAKE PILLS FOR THE REST OF THEIR LIVES.

V.LEE

YEAH, BUT YOU ONLY GAVE ME FOUR.

"It's a beautiful suit, but the legs won't uncross."

Princess cruise lines.

"We *did* do a facelift. Unfortunately there was another one just like it underneath."

Sally Ride describes 153 days in orbit with a spaceman.

Toby Blair proves once and for all that he is indeed engaged to a real, live centerfold.

Beauty College finals.

Getting his wife's hint, Dr. Edwards
sleeps on the couch.

"'Tis the winter of our disco-tent."

Rush Limbo.

"My guess is rheumatism. Best keep him out
of damp places for awhile."

Custer's last birthday party.

Howard Hughes meets CHiPs.

Home Pregnancy Tests for literalists.

"I never let my kids watch this stuff. Too much Saxon violence."

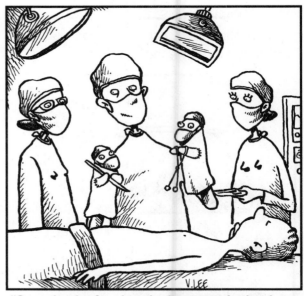

"Sure they're fun, but the best part is that I can bill for two additional specialists."

Reba Gallo wards off the advances of John Merrick, the elephant man.

Victoria Secret's hostile takeover of GQ.

"Well no wonder the refrigerator's warm.
You're out of ice cubes."

"Well, make up your mind. Do you
want school spirit or not?"

Einstein's locker combination.

One day in the Ottoman Empire.

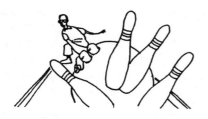

YOU SAY YOU WANT A DIVORCE BECAUSE YOU WERE MARRIED UNDER FALSE PRETENSES?

YES, SIR. I FOUND OUT HER FATHER DIDN'T HAVE A LICENSE FOR THAT GUN.

V. LEE

Memory down trip lane.

The benefits of dry beer.

The trial of Peter Piper.

At the electricians' union Christmas party.

Bill Clinton's lament.

The trouble with beanbag chairs.

"I have to warn you, I'm wearing boxer shorts and I know how to use them."

"Thank goodness. Now I can deposit my virtual paycheck."

My dinner with Joan of Arc.

"Dang kids. Done gone and got themselves stuck up in that palm tree again."

Einstein contemplates a comb.

"Why yes, as a matter of fact, I *was* born in a china closet."

Garth Vader.

Where police sketch artists start out.

The Honey Mooners.

"Honey, is it okay if I go and talk to all the nice people in the audience now?"

"We found a house in your price range.
Unfortunately, there's a Scottish terrier
named Rusty living in it."

900 numbers for losers.

Pippi Longshoreman.

Mike's singing debut was about to take a sudden and gruesome turn.

Okay, now I'm gonna take this horseshoe out of the fire. When I nod my head, hit it.

V. LEE

THE YOUNG APPRENTICE BECOMES THE NEW VILLAGE BLACKSMITH

L. Ron Hubbard's mother.

"Don't act so surprised. The personals ad
clearly stated that I wore glasses."

"My Three Sons" — the later years.

Dr. Jekyll and Mr. Ed.

71

"I'm sorry, ma'am. But this driver's license is only good for covered wagons."

How Mayberry got Goober.

"I'm sorry, boys, but I think there's been some mistake. According to this driver's license, you've captured Ed Asner."

Why more women are becoming astronauts.

Microwave fireplaces.

Cabdriver School.

Amish bikers.

Milk of Amnesia.

James Bond at fifteen.

Salvador Dali Parton.

Autumn in L.A.

Once again, Jarvis Allen forgets brother Angus' birthday.

My date with a super-model.

"I think it's safe to say that 'Gownless Evening Strap' was *not* a label misprint."

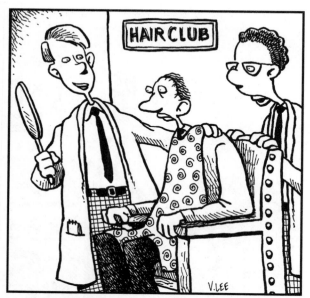

"After analyzing your hair loss pattern, we decided a *skull* reduction was your best bet."

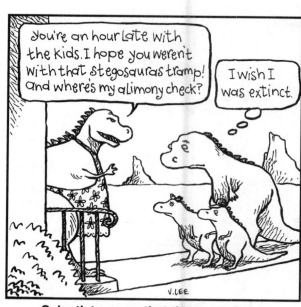

Scientists agree that the most dread creature of the prehistoric age was the horrible Tyrannosaurus Ex.

The slings and arrows of bachelorhood.

George Washington visits the Washington Monument.

"It's an offer from Victoria's Secret. They want to buy back your catalog."

"There I was, deep in the Alzonian brush, when I felt a pair of eyes peering at me from out of the bush. Lo and behold, turns out that's all it was."

Whistler's mother.

The funeral of Lars Thatchel, inventor of the Hokey-Pokey.

The horrors of animal testing.

Unicycle wheelies.

AAAAA Meetings.

"I'm visiting my grandfather here. It's way too expensive to keep him in a rest home."

Captain Kirk finally finds a use for Tribbles.

"Then they shouldn't write 'tip jar' on it, should they?"

The malpractice suit of Dr. Kevorkian.

A hint that your bride-to-be might
be the jealous type.

Beverly Hillbillies 90210.

"Since the world sees America as a nation of the overweight, I've decided to go with vertical stripes for a nice slimming effect."

Kerri Strug: the later years.

Soon after, Lois stopped sharing her candy with Superman.

Classic movie double feature #17.

**"There, I've fixed your recliner, Dr. Ames.
Now it goes all the way back to childhood."**

"It's one of those educational toys that prepares you for life. No matter how you put it together, it's always wrong."

Olive, the other reindeer, used to laugh and call him names.

St. Nickel-less.

How conscience really works.

"I'm really optimistic about my future, but I don't want everybody to know. Do you have anything in a rose-colored contact lens?"

106

"Of course, I'm only interested in my wife's happiness. As a matter of fact, I'm so interested I'm hiring you to find out who's responsible."

The Brim Reaper.

Whistler's Brother.

Yoko Ono Bono.

112

Another ugly case of racism.

"I keep suggesting they fix the hole
in the bottom of the suggestion box,
but they never respond."

Gandhi as a baby.

Life Question #227: How do you throw away a garbage can?

How the pole vault was invented.

At the M&M factory.

117

"Rumor has it Jackson's grilling suspects again."

The life and times of Manny the barber.

The human fly goes to therapy.

Neil Armstrong solves the mystery
of ice on the moon.

"I know this probably isn't the best time to tell you this — but, Alma, I'd like a trial separation."

The first draft of the Declaration of Independence.

Bartlett gets his start.

John Gotti: the early years.

"My toupee's made of dog hair. It does this every time I get near a tree."

What's wrong? It's what you asked for, right? A sexy 2-piece outfit for the bedroom